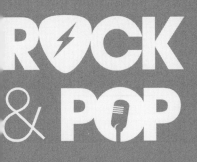

THE EXAM AT A GLANCE

For your Rock & Pop exam you will need to perform a set of **three songs** and one of the **Session skills** assessments, either **Playback** or **Improvising**. You can choose the order in which you play your set-list.

Song 1

Choose a song from this book

OR from www.trinityrock.com

Song 2

Choose a different song from this book

OR from www.trinityrock.com

OR perform a song you have chosen yourself: this could be your own cover version or a song you have written. It should be at the same level as the songs in this book. See the website for detailed requirements.

Song 3: Technical focus

Choose one of the Technical focus songs from this book, which cover three specific technical elements.

Session skills

Choose either **Playback** or **Improvising**.

When you are preparing for your exam please check on **www.trinityrock.com** for the most up-to-date information and requirements as these can change from time to time.

CONTENTS

Each song has two backing tracks: the first includes a click track to play along with, the second omits the click track.

Trinity College London's Rock & Pop syllabus and supporting publications have been devised and produced in association with Faber Music and Peters Edition London.

Published by
Trinity College London
www.trinitycollege.com

Registered in England. Company no. 02683033
Charity no. 1014792
Patron HRH The Duke of Kent KG

Copyright © 2012 Trinity College London
First published in 2012 by Trinity College London

Fourth impression, May 2015

Cover and book design by Chloë Alexander
Brand development by Andy Ashburner @ Caffeinehit (www.caffeinehit.com)
Photographs courtesy of Rex Features Limited
Printed in England by Caligraving Ltd

Audio produced, mixed and mastered by Tom Fleming
Drums arranged by George Double
Backing tracks arranged by Tom Fleming
Musicians
Vocals: Bo Walton, Brendan Reilly & Alison Symons
Keyboards: Oliver Weeks
Guitar & Bass: Tom Fleming
Bass: Ben Hillyard
Drums: George Double
Studio Engineer: Joel Davies www.thelimehouse.com

All rights reserved

ISBN: 978-0-85736-246-9

SONGS JUMP INTO THE FOG

demo backing
2 with click
3 without click

The Wombats
Words and Music by Matthew Murphy, Daniel Haggis and Tord Knudsen

SONGS GREEN RIVER

TRACK 4 demo
TRACK 5-6 backing
5 with click
6 without click

Creedence Clearwater Revival
Words and Music by John Fogerty

♩ = 126 **Rock** *2 bars count-in*

SONGS FREIGHT TRAIN

TRACK 7 demo
TRACK 8-9 backing
8 with click
9 without click

Taj Mahal
Words and Music by Paul James, Fred Williams and Elizabeth Cotten

SONGS

TRACK 10
TRACK 11-12
demo backing
11 with click
12 without click

SHEENA IS A PUNK ROCKER

Ramones

Words and Music by Thomas Erdelyi, John Cummings, Jeffrey Hyman and Douglas Calvin

♩ = 160 **Punk Rock** *2 bars count-in*

ROAD TO NOWHERE

In your exam, you will be assessed on the following elements:

1 Rhythmic control

In the introduction, think about the phrasing of the rhythmic patterns: the ♪ notes should feel like they lead into the ♩ notes.

Make sure that your sticks rise by the same amount when you want to play equal notes.

2 Hand and foot co-ordination

Aim for precise co-ordination between the bass drum and hi-hat/snare rhythms in this song. You could practise a variety of snare patterns, keeping a ♩ beat going throughout on bass drum.

Listen carefully for any passages where your co-ordination sounds inaccurate. Practise these sections until you can play them naturally and comfortably.

3 Sticking

You could build the sticking around repeated ♪ notes in one hand.
For a right-handed drummer this would mean:

The final note of the pattern could also be played with the left hand.
Either is fine if it sounds good.

TRACK 13
demo

TRACK 14-15
backing
14 with click
15 without click

ROAD TO NOWHERE

Talking Heads
Words and Music by David Byrne

♩ = 112 **March-like** *2 bars count-in*

Intro

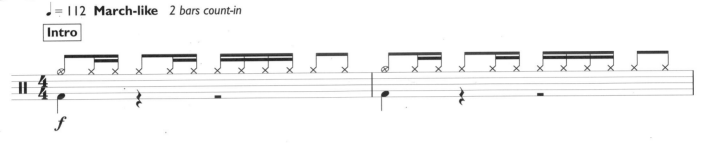

Verse

vocal cue
"We're on a road to nowhere..."

vocal cue
"Feelin' ok this morning..."

vocal cue
"Here we go..."

I BELIEVE I'LL DUST MY BROOM

In your exam, you will be assessed on the following technical elements:

1 Playing a groove

The drums play the same groove for the verses of 'Dust My Broom'. A good drummer would never play all notes at the same volume as this would sound mechanical and unmusical. Think about phrasing the hi-hat in groups of two.

2 Stop time

Bars 15–17 and 23–24 have only one beat per bar – a ♩ on the first beat. This is known as a 'stop-time' section. Make sure that this beat is exactly on time. The first stop-time section features a guitar solo and the second features a bass solo. Listen out for these and make sure you are exactly together with the soloist: count **1 2 3 4 1 2 3 4 1 2 3 4**.

3 Fills

Try to be precise with the fill at bar 18. Don't let it rush – it should flow naturally.

The repeated ♪ notes through bars 25–26 can be really exciting if you judge the *crescendo* carefully. Each note should be slightly louder than the preceding one. Always leave room to push the volume at the end of a long fill: this creates a big, exciting sound.

TECHNICAL FOCUS SONGS

BAND OPTION

I BELIEVE I'LL DUST MY BROOM

Words and Music by Robert Johnson

TRACK 16 · TRACK 17-18
demo · backing
17 with click
18 without click

JUMP INTO THE FOG

The Wombats

'Jump Into The Fog' is taken from the album *This Modern Glitch* (2011), recorded by the Liverpool indie band The Wombats. The three band members met in 2003 at LIPA (Liverpool Institute of Performing Arts) – founded by Paul McCartney in the building which housed his old school. With their upbeat indie pop sound, The Wombats have had several hits – 'Jump Into The Fog', with its pessimistic lyrics and use of minor chords, is darker than most of their songs.

PERFORMANCE HINTS & TIPS

There are two main ideas in 'Jump Into The Fog'. The first idea is in the verse: a straight ♪ groove with bass drum ♪ beats in the first half of the bar.

The second idea is in the chorus: it moves between floor tom and snare, over a bass drum ♩ beat. In order to flow smoothly between the different drums, the sticking should be right-left-right-left-right-right-left.

'You *know* that *we* hit the *ground* upright'

GREEN RIVER

Creedence Clearwater Revival

'Green River' is the title track of the 1969 album *Green River* by the Californian band Creedence Clearwater Revival. The band was formed by brothers John (lead singer/ songwriter and guitarist) and Tom Fogerty (rhythm guitarist). The band's energetic sound was a unique combination of rock music and rockabilly (an early form of rock 'n' roll with a strong country music influence), with lyrics influenced by country music.

PERFORMANCE · HINTS & TIPS

'Green River' opens with three bars' rest for the drums. You will need to count carefully to make sure that you come in at exactly the right place.

The challenge in this song is to master the foot/hand independence of the main groove (starting at bar 5). The ♪ movement on bass drum can be difficult to co-ordinate with a steady ♩ in the right hand. Practise the pattern with a metronome: begin at 60 bpm and gradually build up the speed when you are satisfied that your hands and feet are working well together.

'Let me .remember things I love'

FREIGHT TRAIN

Taj Mahal

'Freight Train' was written in the early 20th century by Elizabeth Cotten, when she was only 12 years old. She was self-taught and played the guitar left-handed, but without restringing it, so used her thumb to play the melody and fingers to play bass and harmony. She did not start recording and performing in public until she was in her sixties, but still went on to win major awards.

'Freight Train' became very popular during the American folk revival in the 1950s and 1960s, when many artists covered it, including Peter, Paul and Mary, and Joan Baez. It is now considered to be an American folk classic. This version is based on the cover by the American blues musician Taj Mahal.

The time signature of 'Freight Train' is $\frac{2}{2}$. This means that although there are four ♩ in a bar (as in $\frac{4}{4}$), there is a strong two 𝅗𝅥 beats-in-a-bar feel.

'Freight Train' uses a country two-in-a-bar feel on both hi-hat and ride cymbal. Aim to make the patterns bounce to give a sense of moving forward without rushing. Make sure that you keep a steady beat in the intro.

Feel the weight of the two main beats in the outro so that the music flows naturally.

This song is also in the keyboards, vocals, guitar and bass books so you can get together and play it in a band.

'Please *don't tell* what *train* I'm on'

SHEENA IS A PUNK ROCKER

Ramones

The Ramones were an American punk band (some people say the first ever punk band) famous for their appearances at the iconic New York CBGB club. Their music is typical of punk – short energetic songs, raw and chaotic, with simple chord progressions played at breakneck speed and an impenetrable wall of sound – often with distortion and feedback and a raucous half-shouting style of singing.

'Sheena Is A Punk Rocker' is a punk rock classic. It was first released in 1977 on the album *Rocket To Russia*.

The focus of 'Sheena Is A Punk Rocker' is a simple, ♩-based punk groove.

To achieve the authentic 'trashy' hi-hat sound marked on the chart:
- the hi-hat cymbals should be loosely together when struck
- apply some pressure on the hi-hat pedal so that the sound of each stroke is prolonged as the cymbals fizz together.

Make sure there is a clear contrast between the louder trashy hi-hat sound and the tightly closed hi-hat sound of the verse.

'*She* had to break *away*'

ROAD TO NOWHERE

Talking Heads

'Road To Nowhere' is a Talking Heads song from their sixth album *Little Creatures* (1985). Starting out as art-school punks, Talking Heads made a series of critically-acclaimed recordings in the 1970s and 1980s. They often experimented musically, combining funky guitar rock with different styles of music from around the world. *Little Creatures* is their most immediately accessible album – straightforward pop – set to frontman and songwriter David Byrne's esoteric lyrics.

There are two main parts to 'Road To Nowhere'. The first part is a march-like introduction which moves from hi-hat to snare drum and then continues into the verse.

Where the ♫♫ move over the bass drum ♩ beat, be sure that hand and feet are strictly aligned. The second part – in bars 13–20 – is a simple straight ♪ groove.

Play the fills carefully and precisely – but make sure they flow, connecting smoothly to the next section.

'Takin' *that* road to *nowhere*'

I BELIEVE I'LL DUST MY BROOM

Robert Johnson

'Dust My Broom' is a 12-bar blues first recorded by the Mississippi blues singer and guitarist Robert Johnson (1911–1938). Like most blues (early American black music originally performed by one singer accompanied on guitar or banjo), 'Dust My Broom' has four beats in a bar, is built on three chords and has a three-line verse where the second line is a repeat of the first.

Robert Johnson lived a short but turbulent life as a wandering musician and enjoyed little commercial success. Although he only recorded 30 songs, most of these went on to become classics and have had a great influence on many rock musicians today. Hundreds of versions of 'Dust My Broom' have been recorded, notably by Eric Clapton, Led Zeppelin, Bob Dylan, Canned Heat and Fleetwood Mac. Johnson died when he was 26 from drinking poisoned whisky.

PERFORMANCE · HINTS & TIPS ·

This chart uses slash notation (bars 28–37) which is very common in kit writing. Rather than write out the repeated pattern over and over again, writers often use slash bars. The slashes mean that the drummer should continue in the same style.

Slash notation is often used for a groove (a section with the same repeated rhythm). Once the groove of a tune has been established, the drummer's role is to continue keeping solid and consistent time.

This song is also in the keyboards, vocals, guitar and bass books so you can get together and play it in a band.

'I *believe* I'll *go* back *home*'

PLAYBACK

For your exam, you can choose either Playback or Improvising (see page 19).
If you choose Playback, you will be asked to play some music you have not seen or heard before. In the exam, you will be given the song chart and the examiner will play a recording of the music. You will hear several two-bar phrases on the recording: you should play each of them straight back in turn. There's a rhythm track going throughout, which helps you keep in time. There should not be any gaps in the music.

In the exam you will have two chances to play with the recording:
- First time – for practice
- Second time – for assessment.

You should listen to the audio, copying what you hear; you can also read the music from the song chart. Here are some practice song charts which are also on the CD in this book.

Don't forget that the Playback test can include requirements which may not be shown in these examples, including those from earlier grades. Check the parameters at www.trinityrock.com to prepare for everything which might come up in your exam.

Practice playback 1

Practice playback 2

IMPROVISING

For your exam, you can choose either Playback (see page 18), or Improvising. If you choose to improvise, you will be asked to improvise over a backing track that you haven't heard before in a specified style.

In the exam, you will be given a song chart and the examiner will play a recording of the backing track. The backing track consists of a passage of music played on a loop. You should improvise a drum beat over it.

In the exam you will have two chances to play with the recording:
- First time – for practice
- Second time – for assessment.

Here are some improvising charts for practice which are also on the CD in this book. Don't forget that the Improvising test can include requirements which may not be shown in these examples, including those from earlier grades. Check the parameters at www.trinityrock.com to prepare for everything which might come up in your exam.

Practice improvisation 1

♩ = 120 **Heavy Rock**

| Em | Am | C | G |

Practice improvisation 2

♩ = 94 **Pop**

| G | D | C | Am |

CHOOSING A SONG FOR YOUR EXAM

There are lots of options to help you choose your three songs for the exam. For Songs 1 and 2, you can choose a song which is:

- from this book
- from www.trinityrock.com

Or for Song 2 you can choose a song which is:

- sheet music from a printed or online source.
- your own arrangement of a song or a song you have written yourself (see page 21).

You can play the song unaccompanied or with a backing track (minus the drums). If you like, you can create a backing track yourself (or with friends), or you could add your own vocals – or both.

For Grade 1, the song should last between one and three-and-a-half minutes, and the level of difficulty should be similar to your other songs. When choosing a song, think about:

- Does it work on my instrument?
- Are there any technical elements that are too difficult for me? (If so, perhaps save it for when you do the next grade.)
- Do I enjoy playing it?
- Does it work with my other pieces to create a good set-list?

See www.trinityrock.com for further information and advice on choosing your own song.

SHEET MUSIC

You must always bring an original copy of the book or a download sheet with email certificate for each song you perform in the exam. If you choose to write your own song you must provide the examiner with a copy of the sheet music. Your music can be:

- a lead sheet with lyrics, chords and melody line
- a chord chart with lyrics
- a full score using conventional staff notation
- see page 21 for details on presenting a song you have written yourself.

The title of the song and your name should be on the sheet music.

WRITING YOUR OWN SONG

You can play a song that you have written yourself for one of the choices in your exam. For Grade 1, your song should last between one and three-and-a-half minutes, so it is likely to be quite straightforward. It is sometimes difficult to know where to begin, however. Here are some suggestions for starting points:

- **A melody**: many songs are made up around a 'hook' (a short catchy melodic idea, usually only a few notes long).
Try writing a couple of ideas for hooks here:

- **A chord sequence**: a short chord sequence can provide an entire verse or chorus. Write your ideas for a chord sequence here:

- **A rhythm**: a short repeated rhythm will often underpin an entire song.
Think of a couple of short rhythms you could use here:

There are plenty of other ways of starting: perhaps with a riff or a lyric, for example.

You will also need to consider the **structure** of your song (verse and chorus, 12-bar blues, and so on), the **style** it is in (blues, hard rock, etc.), and what **instruments** it is for (solo drums or voice/keyboards/drums . . .).

There are many choices to be made – which is why writing a song is such a rewarding thing to do.

WRITING YOUR SONG DOWN

Rock and pop music is often written as a **lead sheet** with the lyrics (if there are any), chords and a melody line.

- As a drummer, you may want to write your part using **drum notation**, used for the songs in this book. There is a guide to this notation on page 24.

- You can, if you prefer, use a **graph** or **table** to represent your music, as long as it is clear to anyone else (including the examiner) how the song goes.

PLAYING IN A BAND

Playing in a band is exciting: it can be a lot of fun and, as with everything, the more you do it, the easier it gets. It is very different from playing on your own. Everyone contributes to the overall sound: the most important skill you need to develop is listening.

For a band to sound good, the players need to be 'together' – that mainly means keeping in time with each other, but also playing at the same volume, and with the same kind of feeling.

Your relationship with the other band members is also important. Talk with them about the music you play, the music you like, and what you'd like the band to achieve short-term and long-term.

Band rehearsals are important – you should not be late, tired or distracted by your mobile phone! Being positive makes a huge difference. Try to create a friendly atmosphere in rehearsals so that everybody feels comfortable trying out new things. Don't worry about making mistakes: that is what rehearsals are for.

'Freight Train' (page 6) and 'Dust My Broom' (page 11) are arranged for band. You will find parts for vocals, guitar, keyboard and bass in the other Trinity Rock & Pop Grade 1 books. Trinity offers exams for groups of musicians at various levels. The songs arranged for bands are ideal to include as part of a set-list for these exams. Have a look at the website for more details.

HINTS AND TIPS

- Plan your band practices in advance. Think about what you would like to do before you get there.

- Record your practice sessions and listen back for sections that worked well and bits that had problems.

- In some songs you will play a supporting role; at other times you may take more of a lead. In both cases you need to listen to the overall group as well as to your own part. Be aware of how you affect the overall sound.

PLAYING WITH BACKING TRACKS

The CD contains demos and backing tracks of all the songs in the book. The additional songs at www.trinityrock.com also come with demos and backing tracks.

- In your exam, you should play with the backing track, or you can create your own (see below).
- The backing tracks start with a click track, which sets the tempo and helps you start accurately.
- Be careful to set the balance between the volume of the backing track and your instrument.
- Listen carefully to the backing track to ensure you are playing in time.

If you are creating your own backing track here are some further tips:
- Make sure the sound quality is of a good standard.
- Think carefully about the instruments/sounds you are putting on the backing track.
- Avoid copying what you are playing on the backing track – it should support not duplicate.
- Do you need to include a click track at the beginning?

COPYRIGHT IN A SONG

If you are a singer or songwriter it is important to know about copyright. When someone writes a song or creates an arrangement they own the copyright (sometimes called 'the rights') to that version. The copyright means that other people cannot copy it, sell it, perform it in a concert, make it available online or record it without the owner's permission or the appropriate licence. When you write a song you automatically own the copyright to it, which means that other people cannot copy your work. But just as importantly, you cannot copy other people's work, or perform it in public without their permission or the appropriate licence.

Points to remember
- You can create a cover version of a song for an exam or other non-public performance.
- You cannot record your cover version and make your recording available to others (by copying it or uploading it to a website) without the appropriate licence.
- You own the copyright of your own original song, which means that no one is allowed to copy it.
- You cannot copy someone else's song without their permission or the appropriate licence.
- If you would like to use somebody else's words in your own song you must check if they are in copyright and, if so, we recommend you confirm with the author that they are happy for the words to be used as lyrics.
- Materials protected by copyright can normally be used as lyrics in our examinations as these are private performances under copyright law. The examiner may ask you the name of the original author in the exam.
- When you present your own song to the examiner make sure you include the title, the names of any writers and the source of your lyrics.

HELP PAGES

DRUM NOTATION GUIDE

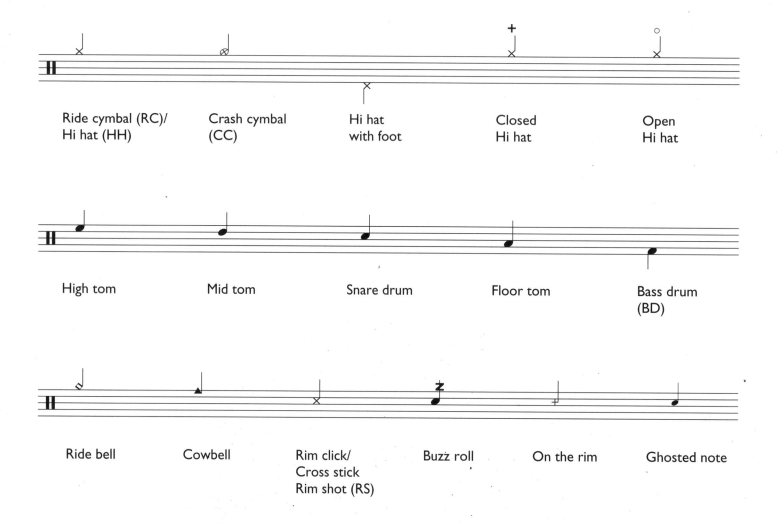

Ride cymbal (RC)/ Hi hat (HH)

Crash cymbal (CC)

Hi hat with foot

Closed Hi hat

Open Hi hat

High tom

Mid tom

Snare drum

Floor tom

Bass drum (BD)

Ride bell

Cowbell

Rim click/ Cross stick Rim shot (RS)

Buzz roll

On the rim

Ghosted note